To Lucinda Morgan Bailey

This is my dog, Clifford.
We do a lot of things together.

We swim together.

We play ball together.

In winter we go sliding together.

One day a man stopped us and asked
if Clifford would like to be in a movie.

Clifford had to take a screen test.
The man told him to act happy.

Clifford acted happy.

Then he asked him to act angry.

Then Clifford pretended to be in love.

The man told him to act frightened. He did.

Clifford acted sad.
The man said Clifford was a terrific actor.
He wanted him to be in a movie.

The next day they took Clifford to Hollywood.

We hated to see him go.

When the movie was finished, everybody said
Clifford was the best actor in the world.
Clifford was a star.

In Hollywood, they built him a big doghouse,
the kind a movie star should have.

They gave him fancy dishes
and brought him special things to eat.

Clifford's dog collars were made of gold and
expensive fur. Some were covered with diamonds.

He even had a swimming pool shaped like a bone.

Clifford loved being a star. They put
his footprint in the cement on Hollywood Boulevard,
just like the other stars.

Everywhere he went he was surrounded
by mobs of movie fans.

They all wanted souvenirs.

His fans were everywhere.

There were a lot of parties. Clifford got tired
of them. But they said movie stars have to go
to a lot of parties.

I saw Clifford on a television talk show.
I thought he looked a little sad.

One day he looked over his wall and saw
a girl playing with her dog. He missed me.

Clifford was tired of being a star.
That night he jumped over the wall.

He left all the fancy dishes and collars
and parties behind.

Clifford came home! And he's home to stay.
He'd rather be with me than in Hollywood.

I'm glad he loves me as much as I love him.

Clifford AND THE GROUCHY NEIGHBORS

Story and pictures by Norman Bridwell

DOGS KEEP OUT!

SCHOLASTIC INC.

New York   Toronto   London   Auckland   Sydney
Mexico City   New Delhi   Hong Kong   Buenos Aires

Do you like dogs? I'm Emily Elizabeth, and
my dog is named Clifford. Most people like him.

But once we had neighbors
who didn't like Clifford at all.

Clifford wanted to make
friends with them anyhow.

Every day he went across the street to visit.
The neighbors acted as if he wasn't there.

Clifford isn't perfect.

He scratches himself as all dogs do.

Sometimes his fur would blow

into the neighbor's yard.

They didn't like that.

And sometimes Clifford snores at night.

Even a little snoring bothered them.

But Clifford liked them.
He liked to listen
to the woman singing.

Once he sang along.

He sang a little too loudly.

Clifford couldn't seem
to do anything right.

When he sat by the fence,
the man complained that Clifford
blocked the sun from his plants.

One day Clifford noticed
that the tree blocked
the sun too. He took care
of the tree for the man.

But the people were not pleased.
Clifford had to put the tree back.

After that I told Clifford to stay away
from the neighbors. We saw them at the shopping
mall. We didn't go near them.

Then Clifford saw their shopping cart roll
away while they opened their car. He tried
to stop the cart.

What a mess.
Poor Clifford.
Poor people.

I told Clifford to never, never go near
the neighbors again.

Clifford stayed on his side
of the street. He would sit
and watch the man feed the birds.
Clifford wished the man
liked him as much as he liked
the birds.

One day Clifford saw some workmen at the
neighbor's house. They were putting in new
water pipes. Clifford went
over to watch.

Clifford could see into the neighbor's yard.
Oh, oh — the birds were in trouble!

Clifford knew he couldn't go in the
neighbor's yard. So he picked up a water pipe
. . . took a deep breath . . .

and vacuumed the cat right out of the yard.
That was a very surprised cat.

The neighbors thanked Clifford
for saving the birds.

"He's not such a bad dog after all," they said.
Good old Clifford.

Clifford's
GOOD DEEDS

Story and pictures by Norman Bridwell

SCHOLASTIC INC.

New York   Toronto   London   Auckland   Sydney
Mexico City   New Delhi   Hong Kong   Buenos Aires

For Tim, Steve, and Paul

Hello. I'm Emily Elizabeth.
This is my dog, Clifford.

A boy named Tim lives across the street.

One day Tim said, "I try to do
a good deed every day. If I had Clifford
I could help a lot of people."
I said, "Let's do some good deeds together."

A man was raking leaves. Tim gave him a hand.
Then we helped him put the leaves in his truck.

I didn't know that dry leaves . . .

. . . make Clifford sneeze.

AH-CHOO

The man said he didn't need any more help.
We went down the street.

We saw a lady painting her fence.

We helped her paint.
When we finished she thanked us.

Clifford felt so happy that he
wagged his tail. That was a mistake.
White paint splattered all over
her house.

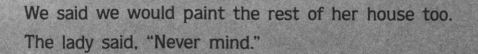

We said we would paint the rest of her house too.
The lady said, "Never mind."

Then we saw an old lady
trying to get her kitten down from a tree.
Tim said, "Clifford, get the kitty."

Clifford bent the limb down
so the lady could reach her kitten.

But his paw slipped.

Clifford moves pretty fast for a big dog.

The lady was glad to get her kitten back.

It didn't take us long to find
our next good deed to do.

Somebody had let the air out of the tires
of a car. The man asked if we could help him.

Tim took a rubber tube out of the car
and stuck it on the tire valve. Then
he told Clifford to blow air through the tube.

Clifford blew.

But he blew a little too hard.

The man felt better
when we took his car to a garage.

We saw a small paperboy.
He was so small that he couldn't throw
the newspapers to the doorsteps.

Clifford gave him a hand. I mean a paw.

Clifford was a little too strong.

Nothing seemed to go right for us.
All our good deeds were turning out wrong.

Then we saw a terrible thing. A man was hurt and lying in the street. Nobody was helping him.

Tim said, "You should never move
an injured person." Clifford didn't hear him.
He picked the man up.

We started off to find a doctor. Oh dear.

We helped the men get their cable
back down the manhole. Tim said, "Clifford,
maybe you shouldn't help me anymore."

Clifford felt very sad. He had tried so hard
to do the right things. We headed for home.

Suddenly we heard somebody shouting,
"Help! Fire!"

The house on the corner was on fire.
Tim ran to the alarm box
to call the fire department.

Clifford ran to the burning house.
There were two little kids upstairs.
With Clifford's help we got them out safely.

Luckily, there was a swimming pool
in the yard.

Clifford put out the fire
just as the firemen were arriving.

The firemen finished the job
and thanked us for our help.

That afternoon the mayor gave us each
a medal for our good deeds.

Of course, Clifford got the biggest medal of all.